John ELDON vawter

THE WINSTON READERS

FIRST READER

BY

SIDNEY G. FIRMAN
SUPERINTENDENT OF SCHOOLS, GLEN RIDGE, NEW JERSEY

AND

ETHEL H. MALTBY
OF CORNING, NEW YORK

ILLUSTRATED BY
FREDERICK RICHARDSON

THE JOHN C. WINSTON COMPANY
PHILADELPHIA   CHICAGO

P–1–23

CONTENTS

THE FOX AND HIS BAG

One day a fox
was going to market.
On the way
he caught a bumble-bee.
He put the bumble-bee
into a bag.
Then he went on.

Soon the fox
came to a house.

He rapped at the door,
"Rap! Rap! Rap!"

A woman came
and opened the door.

The fox said,
"I am going to market.
May I leave my bag here?"
The woman said,
"Yes, you may."

"Do not open the bag,"
said the fox.

Then he went on.

When the fox had gone,
the woman said,
"I wonder
what is in this bag.
I will see."
So she opened the bag.
Out flew the bumble-bee.
A rooster caught him
and ate him up.

By and by
the fox came back.

He looked in the bag
and said,

"Where is my bumble-bee?"

The woman said,

"I just looked in the bag,
and the bumble-bee flew out.
Then a rooster ate him up."

6

The fox said,
"Then give me the rooster."
"Very well," said the woman.
So the fox
ran after the rooster.
He caught him
and put him into the bag.

7

Soon the fox
came to another house.

He went to the door
and rapped,
"Rap! Rap! Rap!"

A woman opened the door.

The fox said,
"I am going to market.
May I leave my bag here?"
"Yes, you may,"
said the woman.

"Do not open the bag,"
said the fox.

Then he went on.

When the fox had gone,
the woman said,
"I wonder
what is in this bag.
I will see."
So she opened the bag.
Out flew the rooster.
A pig caught him
and ate him up.

By and by
the fox came back.

He looked in the bag
and said,
"Where is my rooster?"

The woman said,
"I just looked in the bag,
and the rooster flew out.
Then a pig ate him up."

The fox said,
"Then give me the pig."
"Very well," said the woman.
So the fox ran after the pig.

He caught him
and put him into the bag.

The fox walked on.

Soon he saw another house.

He said,

"I will leave my bag here."

So he rapped,

"Rap! Rap! Rap!"

A woman said,

"Who is there?"

The fox said,

"It is I, the fox.

May I leave my bag here?"

The woman said,

"Yes, you may."

The fox put the bag
on the floor.

"Do not open the bag,"
he said.

Then he went on.

12

When the fox had gone,
the woman said,
"I wonder
what is in this bag.
I will see."
So she opened the bag.
Out jumped the pig.
A little boy ran after the pig.
But the pig got away.

Soon the fox came back.

He looked in the bag
and said,

"Where is my pig?"

The woman said,

"I just looked in the bag,
and the pig jumped out.

My little boy ran after it.

But the pig got away."

14

The fox said,
"Then give me the little boy."
"Very well,"
said the woman.
So the fox took the little boy
and put him into the bag.

At the next house
the fox rapped,
"Rap! Rap! Rap!"

A woman opened the door.

The fox said,
"I am going to market.
May I leave my bag here?
It is very heavy."

The woman said,
"Yes, you may."

So the fox put the bag
on the floor.
"Do not open the bag,"
he said.

Then he went on.

Soon the little boy cried,
"Oh, let me out!
Please let me out!"
The woman opened the bag
and let out the little boy.
Then she put her dog into the bag.

By and by
the fox came back.

He took the bag
and went into the woods.

He said,
"What a fine dinner
I shall have!"

Then he slowly opened the bag.

Out jumped the dog
and caught the fox.

The dog had a fine dinner
that time.

Jack and Jill
Went up the hill
To get a pail of water.
Jack fell down
And broke his crown,
And Jill came tumbling after.

19

THE GREEDY CAT

Once upon a time
White Cat went to visit Gray Mo

Gray Mouse baked a large ca
for White Cat.

She baked a small cake
for herself.

White Cat ate the large cake.
Then he said, "Gray Mouse,
have you any more cakes?"
Gray Mouse said,
"Here is a small cake."
So White Cat
ate the small cake.

Then White Cat said, "Gray Mouse,
have you any more cakes?"

Gray Mouse said,
"No, I have no more cakes."

"Then I shall eat you,"
said White Cat.

And snappety-snap,
down went Gray Mouse.

White Cat went down the road
and met an old woman.

She said,
"You were a greedy cat
to eat Gray Mouse."

White Cat said,
"Yes, I ate Gray Mouse,
and I shall eat you, too."

And snappety-snap,
down went the old woman.

Soon White Cat met
an old man on a donkey.
The old man said,
"You were a greedy cat
to eat Gray Mouse."
White Cat said,
"Yes, I ate Gray Mouse,
and an old woman,
and I shall eat you, too."
And snappety-snap,
down went the old man on a donkey.

White Cat went on till he met
the king and his soldiers.

The king said,
"You were a greedy cat
to eat Gray Mouse."

White Cat said,
"Yes, I ate Gray Mouse,
and an old woman,
and an old man on a donkey,
and I shall eat you, too."

And snappety-snap,
down went the king and his soldiers.

By and by, White Cat
came to some water.

He saw a crab.

The crab said,
"You were a greedy cat
to eat Gray Mouse."

White Cat said,
"Yes, I ate Gray Mouse,
and an old woman,
and an old man on a donkey,
and a king and his soldiers,
and I shall eat you, too."

And snappety-snap,
down went the crab.

The crab said,
"It is too dark in here.
I must get out."

So the crab scratched and scratched.
Soon he made a hole
and jumped out of White Cat.
Then out came
the king and his soldiers,
the old man on a donkey,
the old woman,
and little Gray Mouse.
White Cat sat all day
sewing up the hole
in his coat.

THE THREE GOATS

Once upon a time
there were three goats.
One was Little Billy Goat.
One was Big Billy Goat.
And one was Great Big Billy Goat.

The goats saw some grass
on the mountain.

They wanted to eat the grass.

But they had to cross a bridge
over a river.

Under the bridge lived a troll.

One day Little Billy Goat
started for the mountain.

He went,
"Trip-trap! Trip-trap!"
on the bridge.

The troll said,
"Who is that
going over my bridge?"

Little Billy Goat said,
"It is Little Billy Goat.
I am going to the mountain.
I want to grow fat."

The troll said
in a loud voice,
"Now I am coming
to gobble you up!"

"Oh, do not eat me,"
said Little Billy Goat.
"I am little.
Wait for Big Billy Goat.
He is much bigger."

"Well then,
be off with you!"
said the troll.

So Little Billy Goat went,
"Trip-trap! Trip-trap!"
over the bridge.

31

Soon Big Billy Goat
started for the mountain.
He went,
"Trip-trap! Trip-trap!"
on the bridge.
The troll said,
"Who is that
going over my bridge?"

Big Billy Goat said,
"It is Big Billy Goat.
I am going to the mountain.
I want to grow fat."

The troll said,
"Now I am coming
to gobble you up!"

"Oh, do not eat me,"
said Big Billy Goat.
"Wait for Great Big Billy Goat.
He is much bigger."

"Well then, be off with you,"
said the troll.

So Big Billy Goat went,
"Trip-trap! Trip-trap!"
over the bridge.

At last Great Big Billy Goat
started for the mountain.

He went,
"Trip-trap! Trip-trap!"
on the bridge.

The troll said,
"Who is that
going over my bridge?"

Great Big Billy Goat said,
"It is Great Big Billy Goat.
I am going to the mountain.
I want to grow fat."

The troll said,
"Now I am coming
to gobble you up!"

"Well, come on then!"
said Great Big Billy Goat.
"I am not afraid of trolls.
Come on!"

The troll said,
"Look out then.
I am coming."

The troll tried to catch
Great Big Billy Goat.

But Great Big Billy Goat
went, "Bump!" with his horns.

The troll went over the bridge
into the water.

Down, down he went,
and never came up.

Then the goats ate the grass
on the mountain.

Little Boy Blue,
Come blow your horn.
The sheep's in the meadow,
The cow's in the corn.
Where's the little boy
Who looks after the sheep?
Under the haystack fast asleep.

THE RAINDROP

Once a farmer
had a large field of corn.
He worked hard
to make the corn grow.
But the corn
began to dry up.
Then the farmer said,
"My corn is drying up.
I wish it would rain."

A little raindrop
heard the farmer.
It said,
"I will help the farmer.
His corn is drying up."
"What can you do?"
said a cloud.
"You are only a little raindrop.
You cannot water the corn."

The raindrop said
"I am a little raindrop.
But I can help a little.
So here I go."
Down went the little raindrop.
It fell on the farmer's nose.
The farmer looked up.
He said,
"Was that a raindrop?
Oh! it is going to rain!"

Soon another raindrop fell.

Then another fell,
and another fell.

The other raindrops said,
"If you go, we shall go, too."

So they all went down
and made a hard rain.

Then the corn began to grow.

THE CLOUDS

White sheep, white sheep,
On a blue hill,
When the wind stops,
You all stand still.
When the wind blows,
You all go away.
White sheep, white sheep,
Why won't you stay?

—*Christina G. Rossetti*

42

One to make ready,
   And two to prepare.
Good luck to the winner,
   And away goes the pair.

43

THE DOG AND THE COCK

Once a dog and a cock
went into the woods.

Soon it grew dark.

The cock said,
"Let us stay here all night.
I will sleep in this tree-top.
You can sleep in the hollow trunk."

"Very well," said the dog.

So the dog and the cock
went to sleep.

In the morning
the cock began to crow,
"Cock-a-doodle-do!
Cock-a-doodle-do!"
Mr. Fox heard him crow.
He said,
"That is a cock crowing.
He must be lost in the woods.
I will eat him
for my breakfast."

Soon Mr. Fox
saw the cock
in the tree-top.

He said to himself,
"Ha! ha! Ha! ha!
What a fine breakfast
I shall have!
I must make him come down
from the tree.
Ha! ha! Ha! ha!"

So he said to the cock,
"What a fine cock you are!
How well you sing!
Will you come
to my house
for breakfast?"

The cock said,
"Yes, thank you, I will come,
if my friend may come, too."
"Oh yes," said the fox.
"I will ask your friend.
Where is he?"
The cock said,
"My friend is in this hollow tree.
He is asleep.
You must wake him."

Mr. Fox said to himself,
"Ha! ha! I shall have
two cocks for my breakfast!"

So he put his head
into the hollow tree.

Then he said,
"Will you come to my house
for breakfast?"

Out jumped the dog
and caught Mr. Fox by the nose.

I like little pussy
  Her coat is so warm,
And if I don't hurt her
  She'll do me no harm.
So I'll not pull her tail,
  Nor drive her away,
But pussy and I
  Very gently will play.

THE PLAYMATE

A little princess was not happy.
The queen said,
"What shall we do
to make the princess happy?"
The king said,
"Let us ask Good Fairy
to help us."
"Oh, yes," said the queen,
"let us ask Good Fairy."

So the king called Good Fairy.
He said,
"Good Fairy, can you
make the princess happy?"
"Yes, I can," said Good Fairy.
"Find a playmate
for the princess.
Then she will be happy."

The princess had a cat.

Her name was Trippy.

Trippy heard what Good Fairy said.

So she said,

"Good Fairy, please change me
into a little girl.

Then I can be a playmate
for the princess."

So Good Fairy changed Trippy
into a little girl.

The princess was happy now.
She played with her playmate
all day.

She called her "Playmate."

Once the princess said,
"I wonder where Trippy is!"

Playmate said,
"Oh, Trippy is not far away."

But she did not tell
where Trippy was.

One day a mouse
ran across the floor.

The princess was afraid.

But Playmate was not afraid.

She ran after the mouse
and caught it.

The Princess said, "Playmate,
you run just like Trippy."

Then Good Fairy came back.
She said,
"Trippy, you can never be
a little girl.
You like mice too well."
So she changed Playmate
back into a cat.
The princess said,
"Now I know where Trippy was."

THE BAG OF GOLD

Once there was
a selfish old man.
The old man
had a bag of gold.
One night he said,
"Ah! this gold is mine.
It is all mine,
and I shall keep it for myself."
So he hid the bag of gold
and went to bed.

A robber was looking
through the window.

He saw the old man
hide the bag of gold.

He said,
"When the old man is asleep,
I will get that gold."

So the robber
crept into the house.

He took the bag of gold
and ran away.

There was a little hole
in the bag.

But the robber ran so fast
he did not see the hole.

One piece of gold fell out.

Then another piece fell out.

Soon all the gold
lay by the roadside.

In the morning
a fairy came along.
She saw the gold
by the roadside.
She said,
"Oh, this is the old man's gold.
I will not give it back to him.
He is too selfish.
He would hide it again.
Gold should make some one happy."

So the fairy
touched the pieces of gold
with her wand.

And they turned
into yellow dandelions.

The fairy said,
"Dandelions will make
the children happy."

And that is why
children love dandelions.

THE DANDELION

"O Dandelion, yellow as gold,
What do you do all day?"
"I just wait here
  in the tall green grass
Till the children come to play."

"O Dandelion, yellow as gold,
What do you do all night?"
"I wait and wait
   till the cool dew falls,
And my hair grows long and white."

"And what do you do
    When your hair is white,
And the children come to play?"
"They take me up
    in their dimpled hands,
And blow my hair away."

1st—5

THE WOLF AND THE KIDS

There was once a mother goat.
She had seven kids.
One day she said,
"I am going to market.
Do not open the door
while I am away.
The old wolf will get in
and eat you.
Good-bye, little kids.
Do not open the door."

The wolf saw the mother goat
go away.

He said,
"Now is the time
to eat the kids."

He went to the house
and rapped,
"Rap! rap! rap!"

"Who is there?" asked the kids.

"It is your mother.
I have something for you,"
said the wolf.

"Oh, no! no!" said the kids.
"You are not our mother.
She has a sweet voice.
Your voice is not sweet.
You are the wolf!
Go away!
Go away!
We will not open the door
for you.
Go away!
Go away!"

So the wolf ran away.

Soon the wolf rapped again,
"Rap! rap! rap!"

"Who is there?"
asked the kids.

"It is your mother,"
said the wolf
in a sweet voice.

The kids said,
"Yes, that is our mother's voice.
Let her in!"

But one little kid
looked under the door.

He saw the wolf's black feet.
He cried,
"Oh, no! no!
You are not our mother.
She has white feet.
You have black feet.
You are the wolf!
Go away!
Go away!
We will not open the door
for you.
Go away!
Go away!"

So the wolf ran away.

The wolf ran to the mill.

He said,

"Miller, dust my feet with flour!"

The miller was afraid of the wolf.

So he dusted his feet with flour.

Then the wolf had white feet.

Soon the wolf rapped again,
"Rap! rap! rap!"

"Who is there?" asked the kids.

The wolf said
in a sweet voice,
"It is your mother!"

The kids said,
"Yes, that is our mother's voice."

One little kid
saw the wolf's white feet.
He said,
"Yes, that is our mother.
She has white feet."

So the kids opened the door.

In jumped the wolf!

The little kids cried,
"Oh! it's the wolf!
Run! Run!
It's the wolf!"

They began to hide
under chairs and tables.

The wolf found them
and ate them.

But one little kid
hid in the tall clock.

The wolf looked and looked
but he could not find him.

So he went away.

71

By and by
Mother Goat came home.
   Oh! what did she see?
   The door was open!
   Tables and chairs were upset!
   But she saw no kids!
   She called, "Kids! kids!
Where are you?"
   "Here I am
in the tall clock,"
said the little kid.

Mother Goat
opened the tall clock.

Out jumped the little kid.

Mother Goat asked,
"Where are the other kids?"

The little kid
began to cry.

He said,
"The wolf ate them."

Then Mother Goat said,
"Come, let us find the wolf."

So they went to find the wolf.

They found the wolf asleep
under some trees.

Mother Goat saw something move
inside the wolf.

She said,
"Are my kids alive?
I shall see."

So she took her scissors
and cut open the wolf.

Then out jumped the six kids.

Mother Goat said,
"Now get some large stones."

The kids got six large stones.

Mother Goat put the stones
inside the wolf.

Then she sewed up the hole.

"Come, let us go home now,"
said Mother Goat.

So the seven kids went home
with Mother Goat.

Soon the wolf awoke.

He said,

"How thirsty I am!

I must have a drink."

He went down to the brook.

But splash!

he fell into the water.

The stones were so heavy

he could not get up.

And that was the end of the wolf.

Little Jack Horner
Sat in a corner,
Eating his Christmas pie.
He put in his thumb
And pulled out a plum,
And said,
"What a good boy am I!"

TITTY MOUSE AND TATTY MOUSE

Once upon a time,
there were two little mice.
One was Titty Mouse.
One was Tatty Mouse.

Titty Mouse lived
in a little house.
Tatty Mouse lived
in a little house.
So they both lived
in a little house.
Titty Mouse went
to find something for supper.
Tatty Mouse went
to find something for supper.
So they both went
to find something for supper.
Titty Mouse
found a bag of meal.
Tatty Mouse
found a bag of meal.
So they both
found a bag of meal.

Titty Mouse
made a pudding for supper.
Tatty Mouse
made a pudding for supper.
So they both
made a pudding for supper.
Titty Mouse
put her pudding on the stove.
Tatty Mouse
put her pudding on the stove.
**Titty Mouse upset her pudding
and killed herself.**

Tatty Mouse
sat down and cried.

The little stool said,
"Why do you weep, Tatty Mouse?"
Tatty Mouse said,
"Titty is dead,
and so I weep."
Then the little stool said,
"I shall hop."

So the little stool hopped.

The broom said,
"Little Stool, why do you hop?"
The little stool said,
"Titty is dead,
and Tatty weeps,
and so I hop."
Then the broom said,
"I shall sweep."

So the broom swept.

The door saw the broom sweep.
The door said,
"Broom, why do you sweep?"
The broom said,
"Titty is dead,
and Tatty weeps,
and the stool hops,
and so I sweep."
Then the door said,
"I shall slam."
So the door slammed.

The window
heard the door slam.

The window said,
"Door, why do you slam?"

The door said,
"Titty is dead,
and Tatty weeps,
and the stool hops,
and the broom sweeps,
and so I slam."

Then the window said,
"I shall rattle."

So the window rattled.

84

The old bench
heard the window rattle.

The old bench said,
"Window, why do you rattle?"

The window said,
"Titty is dead,
and Tatty weeps,
and the stool hops,
and the broom sweeps,
and the door slams,
and so I rattle."

Then the old bench said,
"I shall run around the house."

So the old bench
ran around the house.

The ax saw the old bench
run around the house.

The ax said,
"Old Bench, why do you
run around the house?"

The old bench said,
"Titty is dead,
and Tatty weeps,
and the stool hops,
and the broom sweeps,
and the door slams,
and the window rattles,
and so I run around the house."

Then the ax said,
"I shall cut."

So the ax cut.

The old tree
heard the ax cut.

The old tree said,
"Ax, why do you cut?"

The ax said,
"Titty is dead,
and Tatty weeps,
and the stool hops,
and the broom sweeps,
and the door slams,
and the window rattles,
and the old bench
runs around the house,
and so I cut."

Then the old tree said,
"I shall fall."

So the old tree fell.

And it broke the house.

and the stool,

and the broom,

and the door,

and the window,

and the old bench,

and the ax.

The noise frightened Tatty Mouse.

She ran away

and never came back again.

There was an old man,
And he had a calf,
And that is half.
He took him out of the stall,
And put him on the wall,
And that is all.

THE CLEVER MOUSE

A STORY TO PLAY

TIME—Once upon a time. PLACE—In a barn.
Pussy has caught Squeaky.

Pussy: Now, Squeaky,
  I am going to eat you.
Squeaky: Kind Pussy,
  may I speak
  before you eat me?
Pussy: What have you to say,
  Squeaky?

Squeaky: Pussy, will you
    wash your face
    before you eat me?
    Nice cats wash their faces
    before they eat.

Pussy: You are right, Squeaky.
    I am a nice cat.
    I will wash my face
    before I eat you.

(Pussy drops Squeaky.
Squeaky runs away.)

Squeaky: Ha! ha! Pussy.

You may be a nice cat.

But you are not a wise cat.

Pussy: You are a sly little mouse.

Next time I shall wash my face

after I eat.

Evening red and morning gray
Sends the traveler on his way.
Evening gray and morning red
Brings down rain upon his head.

THE LITTLE PORRIDGE POT

Once a little girl
and her mother lived alone.
Their house was near the woods.
They were very, very poor.

One morning the mother said,
"There is nothing to eat
in the house.
Will you go into the woods
and pick some berries?"

The little girl said,
"Yes, Mother, I will."
So she went into the woods.

She walked on and on.
Soon she met an old woman.

"What are you doing in the woods?"
said the old woman.

"I am going to pick berries
for breakfast,"
said the little girl.

The old woman said,
"Little girl,
here is a porridge pot.
When you are hungry, say,
'Little Pot, boil!'
Then it will make porridge for you.
When you say,
'Little Pot, stop!'
it will stop."

"Oh, thank you,"
said the little girl.

The little girl ran home.
"Look, Mother, look!"
she cried.
"See this porridge pot."
Then she said,
"Little Pot, boil!"
And the pot
made a pot of porridge.
Then the little girl said,
"Little Pot, stop!"
And the pot stopped boiling.

Every morning the little girl
took the porridge pot.

She said,
"It is breakfast time.
Little Pot, boil!"

And the little pot
made a pot of porridge
for breakfast.

Then she said,
"That is all we need.
Little Pot, stop!"

And the pot stopped boiling.

So the little girl and her mother
had plenty to eat.

One day the little girl
went away.

By and by
her mother was hungry.

She said,
"Little Pot, boil."

And the pot boiled.

Soon it was full
of porridge.

But the mother
could not stop it.

The pot boiled and boiled.
The porridge ran over
on the floor.
But the mother
could not stop it.
Then the porridge ran
all over the house.
It ran down the street.
But still the mother
could not stop it.

Soon the porridge
ran into the houses.

The people ran out
into the streets.

They cried,
"Stop the porridge!
Stop the porridge!"

But no one
could stop the porridge.

It ran until it came
to the little girl.

The little girl
saw the porridge.

She cried,
"Oh, the porridge pot
is boiling!
Little Pot, stop!"

And the pot stopped boiling.

Then the porridge stopped running.

And all the people
had to eat
their way home again.

Star light, star bright,
First star I see to-night,
I wish I may, I wish I might,
Have the wish I wish to-night.

A LITTLE BOY'S DREAM

A little boy was dreaming
Upon his nurse's lap,
That the pins
    fell out of all the stars,
And the stars
    fell into his cap.

So when his dream was over,
What did that little boy do?
He went and looked
   inside his cap,
And found it was not true.

FINDING THE STARS

Once a little girl
grew tired of her toys.
Then she wanted to play
with the stars.
So she went out
to find them.

Soon the little girl
came to a pond.

She said,
"Pond, where can I find the stars?"

The pond said,
"The stars shine in my face
every night.
Jump in,
then you will find them."

So the little girl jumped in.

But the stars were not there.

The little girl went on
till she met some fairies.

She said,

"Where can I find the stars?"

The fairies said,

"They shine on us every night.
Come and dance with us.
Then you will find them."

So the little girl
danced and danced.

But she did not find the stars.

By and by the little girl
met an elf.

She said,
"Elf, where can I find the stars?"

The elf said,
"Ask Four-Feet
to take you to No-Feet.
Ask No-Feet to take you
to Stairs-With-No-Steps.
Walk up them.
Then you will find the stars."

Soon the little girl
met a horse.

She said, "Are you Four-Feet?"

The horse said,
"Yes, I am Four-Feet."

"Oh," said the little girl,
"will you take me to No-Feet?"

The horse said,
"Jump on my back.
Then I will take you to No-Feet."

They went on
till they came to the sea.
A fish swam to meet them.
The little girl said,
"Fish, are you No-Feet?"
The fish said,
"Yes, I am No-Feet."
"Oh," said the little girl,
"then you will take me
to Stairs-With-No-Steps."
"Jump on my back,"
said the fish.
"Then I will take you
to Stairs-With-No-Steps."

By and by they
swam to a rainbow.
The fish said,
"Here are Stairs-With-No-Steps."

Then the little girl
tried to walk up the rainbow.
But she fell back, splash,
into the sea!
She opened her eyes,
and the rainbow was gone!
"Oh, what a long dream!"
said the little girl.

Hark! Hark!

The dogs do bark.

The beggars are coming to town.

Some in rags,

Some in tags,

And some in velvet gowns.

PETER RABBIT

Once upon a time,
there were four little rabbits.
They were Flopsy, Mopsy,
Cotton-tail, and Peter.
They lived with Mrs. Rabbit
under the roots of a big tree.

One morning Mrs. Rabbit said,
"Now, my dears,
I am going to the baker's.
You may go out to play.
But do not go
into Mr. McGregor's garden.
Your father had an accident there.
Mrs. McGregor put him into a pie.
So do not go
into Mr. McGregor's garden!
Good-bye! Be good children!"

Flopsy, Mopsy, and Cotton-tail
were good little rabbits.

They went down the lane
to gather blackberries.

But Peter was a naughty rabbit.
He ran away
from Flopsy, Mopsy, and Cotton-tail.

He squeezed under the gate,
and ran into Mr. McGregor's garden.

Peter ate some lettuce.
Then he ate some beans
and some radishes.

He ate and ate.
He ate so much
that he began to feel sick.

So he went
to look for some parsley.

116

Mr. McGregor was in the garden planting cabbages.

He saw Peter
looking for parsley.

He jumped up
and ran after him.

"Stop thief! Stop thief!"
cried Mr. McGregor.

But Peter ran on.

Peter was very much frightened!

He ran so fast
that he lost his shoes.

He almost ran away
from Mr. McGregor.

But the big buttons
on his jacket
caught in a net.

Then he could not get away.

Peter pulled and pulled,
but he could not get away.
Then he began to cry.

Some birds heard him.
They came and sang,
"Do not give up!
Pull, Peter, pull!"

So Peter gave one hard pull
and got away.

Mr. McGregor ran after Peter.
He tried to catch him in a pan.
But Peter slipped out of his coat
and got away again.

He ran into a shed.
Then he jumped into a can
to hide from Mr. McGregor.

Mr. McGregor ran into the shed.
He looked and looked,
but he could not find Peter.

He was just going away
when Peter sneezed,
"Ker-choo! Ker-choo!"

Mr. McGregor cried,
"Oh, I see the thief!"
But Peter jumped out of the can
and ran away.

Then Mr. McGregor went back
to his work.

Peter sat down to rest.

Soon an old mouse came along.

She was carrying peas
to her children.

Peter said,
"Can you tell me
the way to the gate?"

The mouse had a large pea
in her mouth.

She could not answer.

Then Peter began to cry again.

The birds heard Peter cry.
They came and sang,
"Do not give up, Peter!
Do not give up, Peter!"
Then Peter tried again
to find the gate.
He saw a white cat.
Peter was afraid of cats.
So he ran back to the shed.

On the way to the shed
Peter heard a noise.
"Scratch-scratch!
Scratch-scratch!"

It was Mr. McGregor
hoeing onions.
And back of Mr. McGregor
was the gate!

Mr. McGregor saw Peter
and ran after him.

But Peter
squeezed under the gate
and ran away.

He never stopped running
until he got home.

Mr. McGregor went back
to his work.

He saw Peter's jacket and shoes
in the net.

He said,
"That little rabbit
shall not get these again."

So he put them on a pole.

Then he said,
"This scare-crow
will frighten the birds."

Peter was very tired!
He was too tired
to eat his supper.

He lay down on the floor
and went to sleep.

But Flopsy, Mopsy, and Cotton-tail
were good little rabbits.
They had blackberries and cream
for supper.

How many days

   has my baby to play?

Saturday, Sunday, Monday,

Tuesday, Wednesday,

   Thursday, Friday,

Saturday, Sunday, Monday.

LIST OF WORDS TAUGHT IN THE WINSTON FIRST READER

bag
going
market

4
am
leave

5
wonder
rooster

7
Very
well

8
another

12
floor

16
next
heavy

18
slowly

19
Jack
Jill
pail
fell
crown
tumbling

20
Greedy
White
Gray
large
cake
small
herself

21
any
more

22
snappety-snap

23
road

24
donkey

25
king
soldiers

26
crab
dark
must

27
scratched
hole
sewing
coat

28
Billy

29
mountain

cross
bridge
river
troll

30
started
Trip-trap

31
loud
coming
gobble
much
bigger
be

34
last

36
Bump
horns

Blue
blow
sheep
meadow
corn
haystack
fast
asleep

38
Raindrop
field
worked
dry
wish

39
cloud
only
cannot

41
other

42
wind
stand
won't
stay

43
ready
two
prepare
luck
winner
pair

44
cock
tree
top
hollow
trunk

45
crow
Cock-a-doodle-do

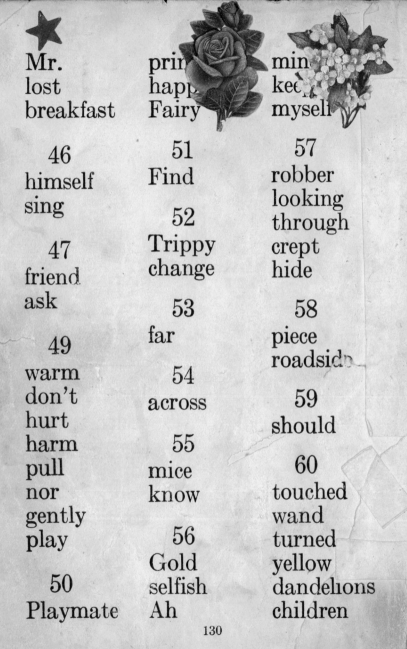

Mr.
lost
breakfast

prin
happ
Fairy

min
kee
myself

46
himself
sing

47
friend
ask

49
warm
don't
hurt
harm
pull
nor
gently
play

50
Playmate

51
Find

52
Trippy
change

53
far

54
across

55
mice
know

56
Gold
selfish
Ah

57
robber
looking
through
crept
hide

58
piece
roadside

59
should

60
touched
wand
turned
yellow
dandelions
children

as
tall
green

62
cool
dew
falls
hair
long

63
take
their
dimpled
hands

64
Wolf
Kids
mother
seven

while
Good-bye

66
something
our
sweet

68
black
feet

69
Miller
dust

71
them
clock

74
move
inside
scissors
six

stones
sewed

76
awoke
thirsty
brook
splash

77
Horner
corner
Christmas
pie
thumb
plum

78
Titty Mouse
Tatty Mouse

79
both

supper
meal

80
pudding
stove
killed

81
stool
weep
dead
hop

82
broom
sweep
swept

83
slam

84
rattle

85
bench
around

86
ax

89
calf
half
stall
wall

90
Clever
Story
Place
Kind
speak
before
say

91
wash
face

nice
drops

92
wise

93
Evening
Sends
traveler
Brings

94
alone
poor

95
pick
berries
doing

96
hungry
boil

98
Every
need
plenty

99
full

100
street

101
people
until

102
running

103
Star

104
Dream
nurse's
lap

pins
cap

105
true

106
tired
toys

107
pond
shine

108
fairies
dance

109
elf
Four
Steps

110
horse

111
sea
fish
swam
meet
rainbow

113
Hark
bark
beggars
town
rags
tags
velvet
gowns

114
Peter
Flopsy
Mopsy
Cotton-tail
Mrs.
roots

115
dears
McGregor
garden
father
accident

116
lane
gather
naughty
squeezed
gate
lettuce
beans
radishes
feel
sick
parsley

117
planting
cabbages

thief
shoes
almost
buttons
jacket
net

118
birds
sang
slipped
shed

119
sneezed
Ker-choo

120
rest
carrying
answer

122
hoeing
onions

123
these
pole
scare-crow

124
cream

125
many
baby
Saturday
Sunday
Monday
Tuesday
Wednesday
Thursday
Friday